English BASICS

FOR AGES 4 - 5
KEY STAGE 1

Contents

The alphabet — 3
The letters b and m — 4
The letters g and t — 5
The letters a and r — 6
Making words (1) — 7
Writing names — 8
The letters h and v — 9
The letters e and n — 10
The letters d and s — 11
Making words (2) — 12
Useful words — 13
The letters l and p — 14
The letters c and w — 15
The letters i and q — 16
Making words (3) — 17

Putting words in groups — 18
Sentences (1) — 19
The letters j and o — 20
The letters k and y — 21
Making words (4) — 22
Rhyming (1) — 23
The letters f and z — 24
The letters u and x — 25
Making words (5) — 26
Last letters — 27
The letters sh — 28
The letters ch — 29
Rhyming (2) — 30
The letters th — 31
Sentences (2) — 32
Answers

Ways to help your child at home

Introduction

Basic literacy in the early years involves *letters*, *sounds* and *words*. The following are some simple, everyday activities which you can do at home which will help your child's understanding in these areas.

Activities to help with letter formation

These activities will help with your child's coordination generally:

- play threading activities with beads, buttons and laces
- make things with Play Doh
- do jigsaw puzzles
- play with construction toys (like Lego)
- try any cutting and sticking activities.

When helping your child write letter shapes, concentrate on lower case (small) letters and not capitals. Always encourage your child to begin each letter in the correct place and form the letter in the way shown in the book.

Activities for teaching letter sounds

- play 'I Spy' using the letter sound (e.g. 'buh' not 'bee')
- have fun with sentences and rhymes where all the words begin with the same letter. (For example, say tongue twisters like 'Peter Piper picked a peck of pickled peppers'.)
- make some simple post boxes out of cereal packets
  - label each with a different letter
  - cut out pictures of things beginning with different letters and post them in the correct boxes
- have fun with rhyming. Think of a short word and encourage your child to think up other words that rhyme with it, for example, sun, bun, fun, run
- read lots of nursery rhymes together.

Activities for teaching words

- make large name cards for the family, toys, pets etc. Give your child separate copies of them to match with the original set. Encourage your child to trace or copy them
- make labels for things in your house, e.g. the table, chair, television. Stick them on the appropriate object. Provide copies of them for matching
- make, and read together, simple captions under family photos in the photograph album
- take labels containing names of products from tins and packets when you go shopping
- look out for the same names in the supermarket. Encourage your child to help 'write' your shopping list with you.

Look and learn

There are **26** letters in the **alphabet**.
Each letter can be written in **two** ways.

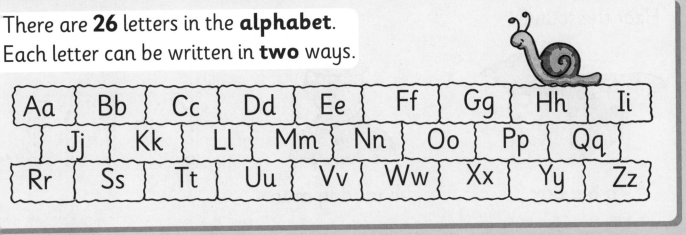

Aa	Bb	Cc	Dd	Ee	Ff	Gg	Hh	Ii
Jj	Kk	Ll	Mm	Nn	Oo	Pp	Qq	
Rr	Ss	Tt	Uu	Vv	Ww	Xx	Yy	Zz

Practice

Fill in the missing letters.

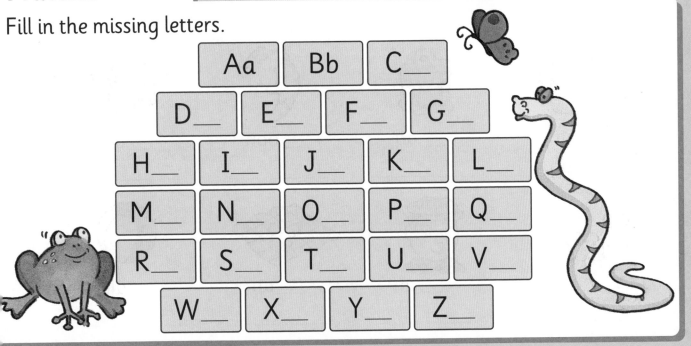

Aa | Bb | C__

D__ | E__ | F__ | G__

H__ | I__ | J__ | K__ | L__

M__ | N__ | O__ | P__ | Q__

R__ | S__ | T__ | U__ | V__

W__ | X__ | Y__ | Z__

Challenge

Join up the letters in order.

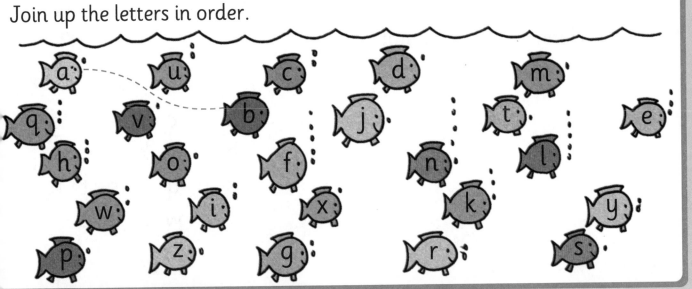

Look and learn

Hear the sounds.

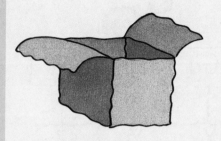

a **b**ig **b**ox

a **m**uddy **m**an

Write the letters.

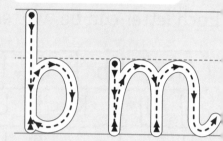

Practice

Choose **m** or **b**.

__m__ug

__mug__

___ag

_____

___oon

_____

___ox

_____

___ed

_____

___an

_____

___ap

_____

___all

_____

Challenge

Draw a **b**oy
with a **b**alloon.

Draw a **m**ouse
on a **m**at.

Find and circle **b** and **m**.

a b c d e f g
h i j k l m n
o p q r s t u
v w x y z

Look and learn

Hear the sounds.

a **g**reedy **g**oat

ten **t**ins

Write the letters.

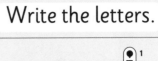

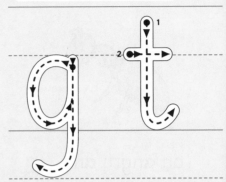

Practice

Choose **g** or **t**.

__girl

girl

___in

_____

___ap

_____

_____

___ate

_____

___oat

_____

"___op"

_____

___oal

_____

___en

_____

Challenge

Draw a **g**orilla with **g**lasses.

Draw a **t**eddy on a **t**able.

Find and circle **g** and **t**.

a b c d e f g
h i j k l m n
o p q r s t u
v w x y z

The letters a and r

Look and learn

Hear the sounds.

an **a**ngry **a**nt

a **r**acing **r**abbit

Write the letters.

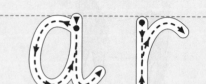

Practice

Choose **a** or **r**.

___ant

ant

___abbit

___at

___pple

___ing

___ug

___mbulance

___rrow

Challenge

Draw an **a**nt on **a**n **a**pple.

Draw a **r**abbit in the **r**ain.

Find and circle **a** and **r**.

a b c d e f g
h i j k l m n
o p q r s t u
v w x y z

Look and learn

Read the words.

rat   bat   b**ag**   r**ag**

Practice

Make some words.

| r | at | b | at | h | at |

_____rat_____

| r | ag | b | ag | t | ag |

_____ _____ _____

Challenge

Write the words.

> Colour the **at** words red.
> Colour the **ag** words blue.

_____bag_____ _____ _____

hat	rag	rat
bag	bat	tag

_____ _____ _____

7

Writing names

Look and learn

We use a capital letter to begin someone's name.

Ben

Sam

Practice

Write each name correctly.

dan
Dan

indira
_____

ali
_____

grace
_____

sue
_____

youssef
_____

emma
_____

fred
_____

Challenge

Draw yourself. Write your name.

Write the name of some friends.

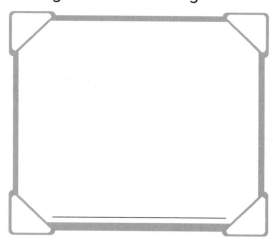

Look and learn

Hear the sounds.

a **h**ot **h**en

a **v**olcano

Write the letters.

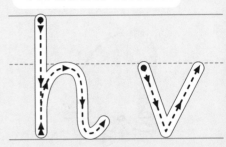

Practice

Choose **h** or **v**.

<u>v</u>olcano

<u>volcano</u>

___en

_____

___an

_____

___est

_____

___ut

_____

___ase

_____

___op

_____

___ill

_____

Challenge

Draw a **h**orse
with a **h**at.

Draw a **v**et
in a **v**an.

Find and circle **h** and **v**.

a b c d e f g
h i j k l m n
o p q r s t u
v w x y z

Look and learn

Hear the sounds.

an **e**gg

nine **n**uts

Write the letters.

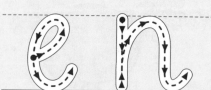

Practice

Choose **e** or **n**.

__net

net

__gg

_____

__est

_____

__ine

_____

__lephant

_____

__uts

_____

nvelope

_____

__lbow

_____

Challenge

Draw **e**ight **e**ggs.

Draw a **n**urse with a **n**et.

Find and circle **e** and **n**.

a b c d e f g
h i j k l m n
o p q r s t u
v w x y z

10

The letters d and s

Look and learn

Hear the sounds.

a **d**ancing **d**og

smelly **s**ocks

Write the letters.

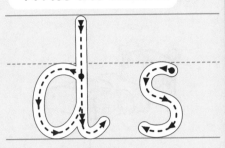

Practice

Choose **d** or **s**.

__sock

sock

__un

_____

__it

_____

__og

_____

__uck

_____

__onkey

_____

__oor

_____

__nake

_____

Challenge

Draw a **d**og eating some **d**inner.

Draw a **s**ock in a **s**ack.

Find and circle **d** and **s**.

a b c d e f g
h i j k l m n
o p q r s t u
v w x y z

Making words (2)

Look and learn

Read the words.

bed

ted

ten

hen

Practice

Make some words.

| b | ed | | t | ed | | r | ed |

____bed____   _____   _____

| h | en | | m | en | | t | en |

_____   _____   _____

Challenge

Write the words.

____ted____

_____

_____

Colour the **ed** words red.
Colour the **en** words blue.

_____

_____

▪

bed	hen	red
men	ted	ten

12

Useful words

Look and learn

Some **words** are very helpful to know.

One, two, three.

the names of numbers

Red, yellow, blue.

the names of colours

Practice

Fill in the missing words in the rhyme.

__one__ , __two__ , _____ , _____ , _____ ,

Once I caught a fish alive.

_____ , _____ , _____ , _____ , _____ ,

Then I let it go again.

number words	
one	two
three	four
five	six
seven	eight
nine	ten

Challenge

blue yellow green red brown orange pink white black

1. Which colour has three letters? _____
2. Which colours have four letters? _____ _____
3. Which colours have six letters? _____ _____
4. Which colours begin with **b**? _____ _____ _____
5. Which colour begins with **g**? _____

13

The letters l and p

Look and learn

Hear the sounds.

lots of letters

pots and pans

Write the letters.

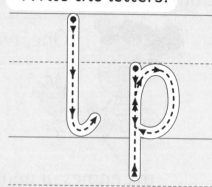

Practice

Choose **l** or **p**.

_pan
pan

___etter

___eg

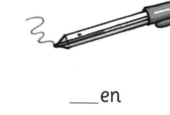

___en

___adder

___eg

___ear

___ock

Challenge

Draw a **p**anda with a **p**en.

Draw a **l**ion on a **l**og.

Find and circle **l** and **p**.

a b c d e f g
h i j k l m n
o p q r s t u
v w x y z

Look and learn

Hear the sounds.

a **c**up of **c**offee

a **w**et **w**orm

Write the letters.

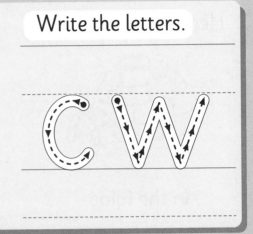

Practice

Choose **c** or **w**.

__w__et

wet

___up

_____

___ag

_____

___at

_____

___ow

_____

___eb

_____

___ar

_____

___indow

_____

Challenge

Draw a **c**amel
with a **c**ap.

Draw a **w**orm
on a **w**all.

Find and circle **c** and **w**.

a b c d e f g
h i j k l m n
o p q r s t u
v w x y z

Look and learn

Hear the sounds.

in the **i**gloo

a **q**uiet **q**ueen

Write the letters.

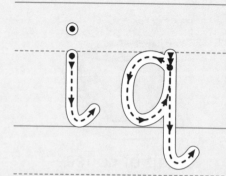

Practice

Choose **i** or **q**.

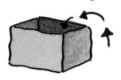

___in

___in___

___nsects

_____

___ll

_____

___ueen

_____

___uestion

_____

___uilt

_____

___uiet

_____

___gloo

_____

Challenge

Draw six **i**nsects.

Draw a **q**ueen in a **q**ueue.

Find and circle **i** and **q**.

a b c d e f g
h i j k l m n
o p q r s t u
v w x y z

Look and learn

Read the words.

 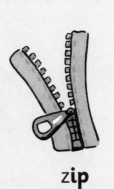  

win   bin   zip   sip

Practice

Make some words.

| w | in | | p | in | | t | in |

_____win_____   _____   _____

| z | ip | | r | ip | | l | ip |

_____   _____   _____

Challenge

Write the words.

Colour the **in** words red.
Colour the **ip** words blue.

_____lip_____   _____   _____

rip	win	pin
zip	tin	lip

_____   _____   _____

Putting words in groups

Look and learn

These are all the names of **animals**.

mouse   tortoise   rabbit

Practice

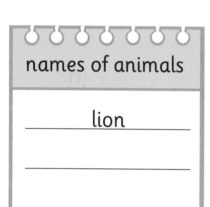

names of animals

lion
_____
_____
_____
_____

Write the names of the animals.

lion   car   monkey   crocodile

bed elephant house   giraffe

Challenge

Write each name in the correct place.

head table arm chair

 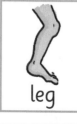

bed leg stool hand

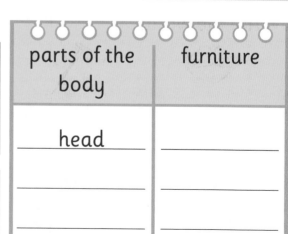

parts of the body	furniture
head	

18

Look and learn

A **sentence** must make **sense**.

I am fly. ☒

I can run. ☑

Practice

Choose the word to finish each sentence.

house   dog   cat   tree   bird

This is a _____.

This is a _____.

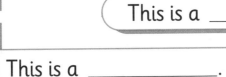

This is a _____.

This is a _____.

Challenge

Write some things you can do.

1. I can play.

2. I can _____.

3. I _____.

4. _____.

5. _____.

play	run
hop	swim
jump	skip
see	hum

Look and learn

Hear the sounds.

a **j**ar of **j**am

an **o**ctopus

Write the letters.

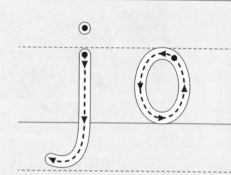

Practice

Choose **j** or **o**.

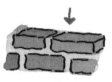

__on

on __

__x

__am

__elly

__ug

__ctopus

__strich

__acket

Challenge

Draw a **j**ug
of orange **j**uice.

Draw an **o**range
octopus.

Find and circle **j** and **o**.

a b c d e f g
h i j k l m n
o p q r s t u
v w x y z

Look and learn

Hear the sounds.

a **k**icking **k**ing

a **y**awning **y**ak

Write the letters.

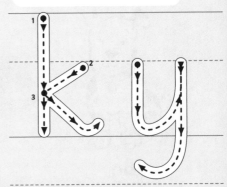

Practice

Choose **k** or **y**.

 __king

king

 ___angaroo

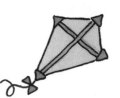 ___ak

 ___ite

 ___awn

 ___oghurt

 ___ey

 ___acht

Challenge

Draw a **k**ettle in a **k**itchen.

Draw a **y**ellow **y**o-**y**o.

Find and circle **k** and **y**.

a b c d e f g
h i j k l m n
o p q r s t u
v w x y z

21

Look and learn

Read the words.

dog   **fog**   **cot**   **pot**

Practice

Make some words.

d | og   f | og   l | og

___dog___   _____   _____

c | ot   d | ot   p | ot

_____   _____   _____

Challenge

Write the words.

Colour the **og** words red.
Colour the **ot** words blue.

        •

___pot___   _____   _____

log	fog	cot
dot	dog	pot

_____   _____

Look and learn

Say these words. Hear the rhyming sound.

| hat | cat | mat | rat |

Practice

Find the pairs of rhyming words.

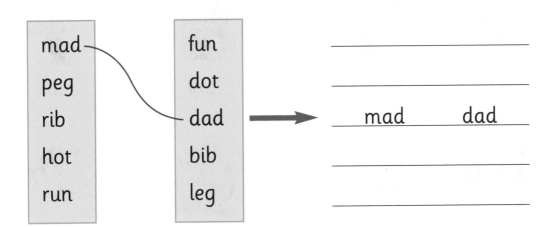

mad	fun
peg	dot
rib	dad
hot	bib
run	leg

_____

_____

mad   dad

_____

_____

Challenge

Circle the word that rhymes.

can	bug	(van)	hid
wet	pet	hop	run
pip	mug	jam	sip
rob	job	pen	fun
hug	pin	rug	not

The letters f and z

Look and learn

Hear the sounds.

a **f**unny **f**ox

a **z**any **z**ebra

Write the letters.

Practice

Choose **f** or **z**.

<u>zi</u>g<u>z</u>ag
zigzag

___an
_____

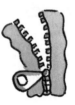
___ip
_____

___ox
_____

___ish
_____

___oo
_____

___ire
_____

___ebra
_____

Challenge

Draw a **f**ox
in a **f**orest.

Draw a **z**ebra
in a **z**oo.

Find and circle **f** and **z**.

a b c d e f g
h i j k l m n
o p q r s t u
v w x y z

Look and learn

Hear the sounds.

an **u**mbrella

a fo**x** in a bo**x**

Write the letters.

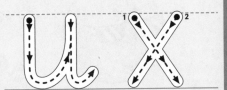

Practice

Choose **u** or **x**.

___under

under

fo___

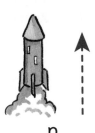

___p

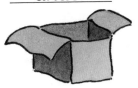

bo___

___mbrella

6

si___

Challenge

Draw a girl **u**nder an **u**mbrella.

Draw a fo**x** in a bo**x**.

Find and circle **u** and **x**.

a b c d e f g
h i j k l m n
o p q r s t u
v w x y z

25

Making words (5)

Look and learn

Read the words.

  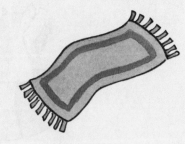 

s**un**   r**un**   r**ug**   j**ug**

Practice

Make some words.

s	un		b	un		r	un

_____ sun _____   _____   _____

j	ug		h	ug		r	ug

_____   _____   _____

Challenge

Write the words.

Colour the **un** words red.
Colour the **ug** words blue.

_____ hug _____   _____   _____

bun	run	hug
rug	jug	sun

_____   _____   _____

Look and learn

Listen to the **last** letter in these words.

cap

cat

can

Practice

Colour the pictures that end with **n**.

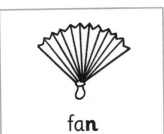

fan

hat

pen

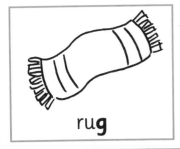

rug

bin

sun

Challenge

Tick ✓ the correct words. Cross ✗ the wrong words.

cub ☐

mat ☐

pot ☐

ten ☐

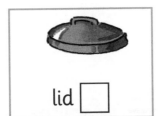

peg ☐

lid ☐

pan ☐

mud ☐

The letters sh

Look and learn

Hear the sound the letters **sh** make.

ship

fi**sh**

Practice

Make some **sh** words.

**ship**
_**ship**_____

fi_____
_____

di_____
_____

_____op
_____

cra_____
_____

_____oe
_____

_____eep
_____

ru_____
_____

Challenge

Sort the words above into sets.

sh at the beginning	sh at the end
ship	fish

Look and learn

Hear the sound the letters **ch** make.

chips

ri**ch**

Practice

Make some **ch** words.

_chips
chips

____eese
_____

ri____
_____

____icken
_____

bun____
_____

tor____
_____

____op
_____

ben____
_____

Challenge

Sort the words above into sets.

ch at the beginning	**ch** at the end
chips	rich

Rhyming (2)

Look and learn

Hear the rhyming words.

a **hat** on a **cat**   a **man** with a **can**

Practice

Choose the word to complete each rhyme.

pen   bin   log   van   box   dish

a <u>dog</u> on a <u>log</u>   a <u>fish</u> in a _____   a <u>tin</u> in a _____

a <u>man</u> with a _____   a <u>fox</u> with a _____   a <u>hen</u> with a _____

Challenge

Think of a rhyming word to go in each space.

1. Jack and **Jill** went up the _____.
2. Little Bo **Peep** has lost her _____.
3. Little Jack **Horner** sat in the _____.
4. Hickery, dickery, **dock**, the mouse ran up the _____.
5. Hey diddle **diddle**, the cat and the _____.
6. Ding dong **bell**, pussy's in the _____.

The letters th

Look and learn

Hear the sound the letters **th** make.

thick

thin

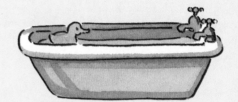
ba**th**

Practice

Make some **th** words.

_thick
___thick___

pa____
_____

mo____
_____

____in
_____

too____
_____

____ief
_____

____ink
_____

ba____
_____

Challenge

Sort the words above into sets.

th at the beginning	**th** at the end
thick	path

Sentences (2)

Look and learn

Sentences must make **sense**.

A dog can moo. ☒   A dog can bark. ☑

Practice

Tick ☑ the sentence if correct.   Cross ☒ the sentence if wrong.

A dog can bark. ☐

A duck can moo. ☐

A bird can sing. ☐

A cow can quack. ☐

A snake can hiss. ☐

Challenge

Complete each sentence.

 A bird lives in a _____.

 A spider lives in a _____.

 A rabbit lives in a _____.

 A horse lives in a _____.

 A fish lives in the _____.

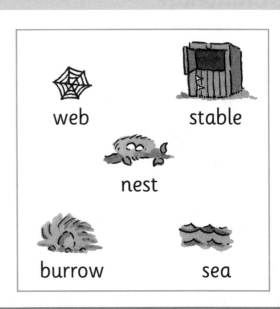

web   stable

nest

burrow   sea